MONSTER TRUCK WORKSHOP

1. Select any shape you want to draw from the "Fronts" design page. Lay the tracing paper on the page, then trace the shape.

2. Select a shape from the "Backs" design page, then trace.

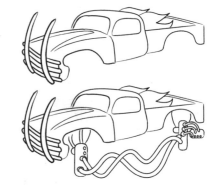

3. Select one of the designs from the "Under-body" section, position it under the car you're drawn, then trace.

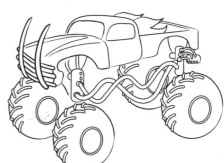

4. Select the tires you want to use from the "Tires" page. Lay the tracing paper on the "Tires" page so the tire is positioned on the front of the truck, then trace. Repeat, repositioning the tracing paper to line up the tires as you go.

5. To put the finishing touches on your custom made Monster Truck, select from the "Extras" pages. Try the body paint details, lights, or have your truck jump the line of cars! Add your own clouds of exhaust, mud splatters, hubcap designs or any other details you dream up!

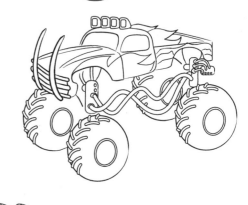

Written by Raymond Miller
Designed and illustrated by Zina Saunders
© 2002 Pace Products, Inc.
333 Semoran Commerce Place, Apopka, FL 32703

Printed in USA
ISBN 1-58295-079-2
1 3 5 7 9 10 8 6 4 2

FRONTS

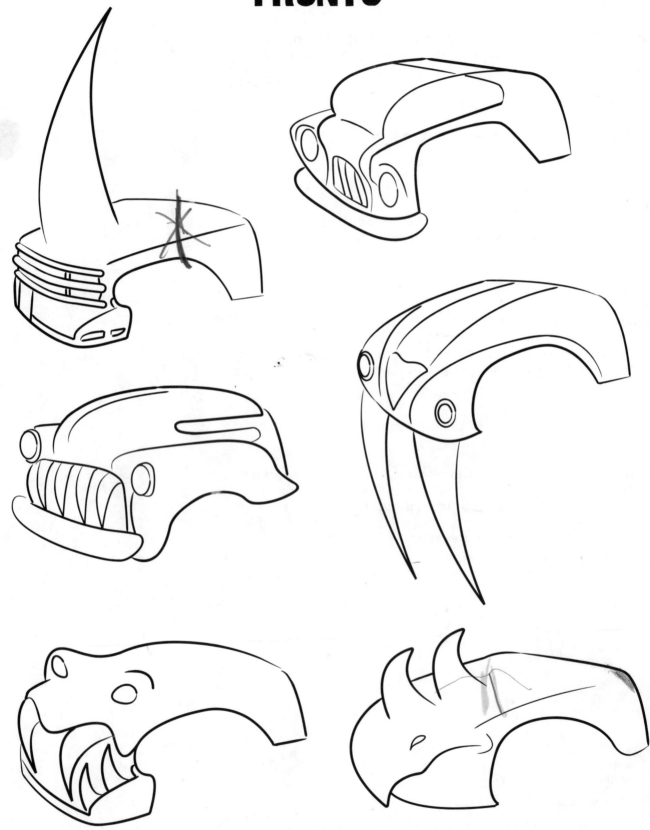

FRONTS

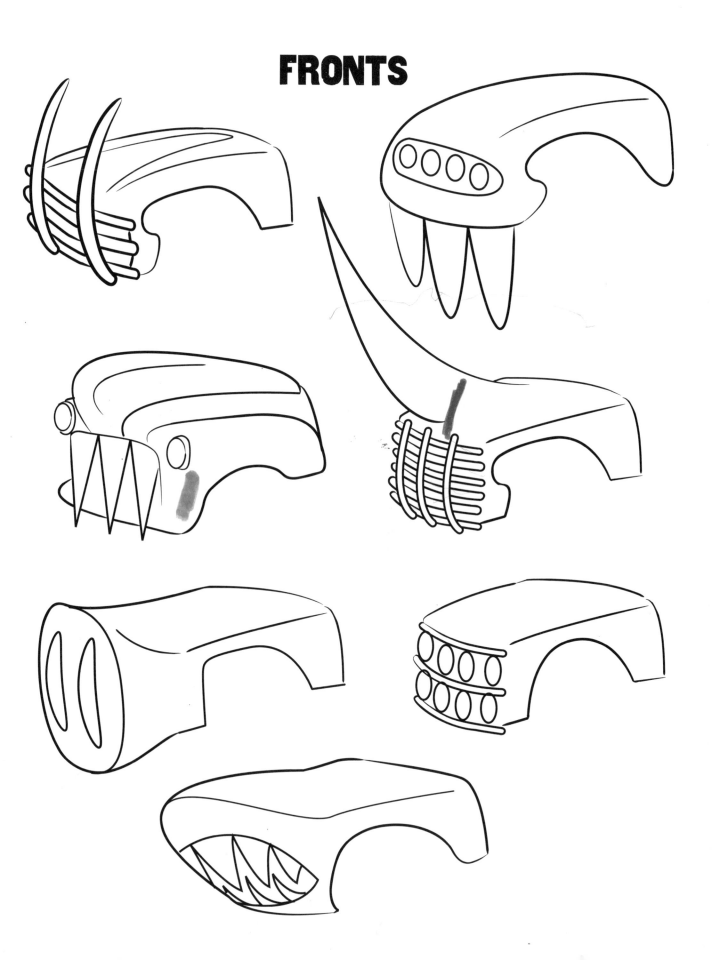

BACKS

LIGHTS

NICKNAMES

ROAD HOG

GHOST RIDER

SCORPION

FRANKIE'S RIG

RAPTOR ATTACK

PAVEMENT POUNDER

MONSTER MASHER

NIGHT MARE

BODY PAINT

UNDER-BODY

EXTRAS

BODY DESIGNS

CAR LINEUP

TIRES

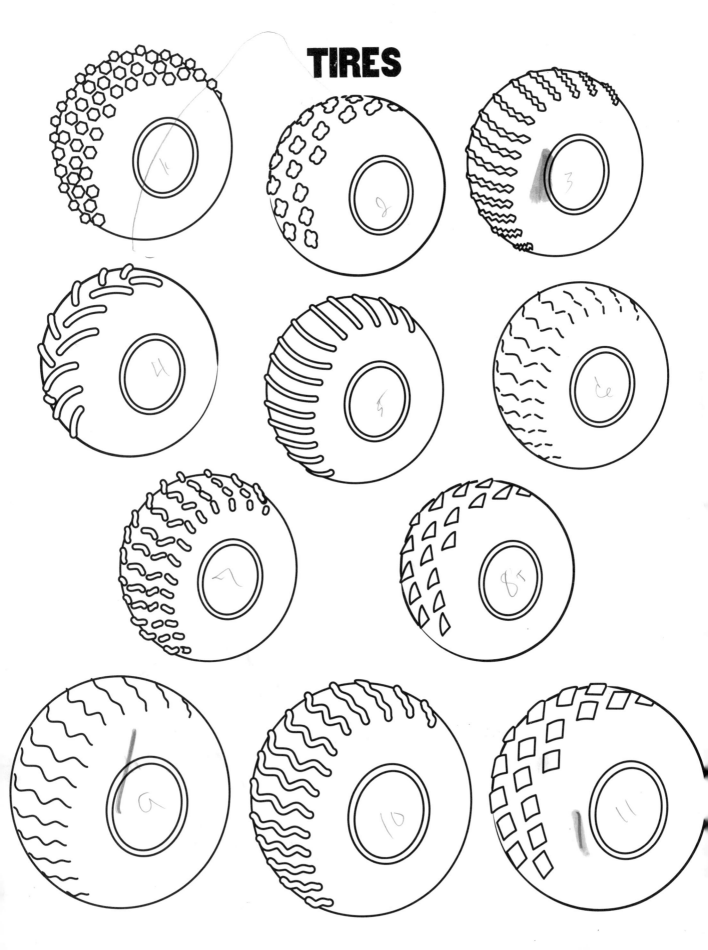

BACKS